A Fresh Approach
to Sight-Reading

Joining the Dots

for Guitar

Grade 4

Alan Bullard and Richard Wright

ABRSM

To the Teacher

Joining the Dots offers lots of material to help build skill and confidence in sight-reading. Used as part of regular lessons and practice, it will help students learn to read new music more quickly and easily, developing their awareness of fingerboard geography, their sense of key and other general musicianship skills.

The five books in the series cover the keys found in ABRSM's sight-reading tests at each of Grades 1–5, with a section for each key. Each section begins with warm-up and technical material ('Key Features' and 'Workouts'), followed by opportunities for improvisation ('Make Music') and several short pieces to sight-read ('Read and Play').

Key Features are a supplement to scales and arpeggios, and will help pupils to establish basic hand shapes and the 'feel' of each key under the fingers. They can be practised at various speeds and dynamics.

Workouts are for exercising and warming up the fingers and hands in the key, and explore a range of techniques. The first of each pair is the same throughout (transposed for each key), to help reinforce key familiarity, while the second is always different.

Make Music provides an opportunity for your pupils to build confidence in (and through) creative and imaginative work, and to develop aural skills. The activities here will also help to familiarize pupils with the 'feel' of the key, but using an approach that is not primarily notation-based. Activities include composing a melody from a given starting-point, and adding a melody with the fingers above a simple open-string thumb part. The ideas here can be used in a flexible way, and the approach and strategy you adopt will probably vary for each student. Encourage your pupils to be as inventive as possible while keeping the features of the chosen key in mind.

Read and Play is the goal of each section – a number of short, characterful pieces, to be played at sight or after a short practice time, with the focus on keeping going. These lead up to and include the technical standard to be found in Grade 4 sight-reading and are a useful source of sight-reading material for those preparing for exams. These pieces may occasionally be slightly longer than the pieces found in Grade 4 sight-reading.

Because the material is arranged to be at an equivalent level in each key, your pupils can 'jump in' to any section, using it alongside pieces, scales or arpeggios that are being learnt in that key. However, within each section it is recommended that pupils learn and play the Key Features and Workouts before moving on to the Make Music and Read and Play material. The suggested fingerings should work for most players but are a recommendation only.

Towards the end of the book you will find **More Pieces to Play**, including longer solo pieces, and some duets and a trio suitable for group work. These can be used in any way you wish – as additional sight-reading practice or as pieces to learn quickly and play through for fun.

First published in 2012 by ABRSM (Publishing) Ltd, a wholly owned subsidiary of ABRSM, 24 Portland Place, London W1B 1LU, United Kingdom

© 2012 by The Associated Board of the Royal Schools of Music

AB 3675

Illustrations by Willie Ryan, www.illustrationweb.com/willieryan
Book design and cover by www.adamhaystudio.com
Music and text origination by Julia Bovee
Printed in England by Caligraving Ltd, Thetford, Norfolk

Dear Guitarist,

Joining the Dots will help you to learn new music more quickly and easily.

In this book you will find a section for each key that you are likely to use.

In each section there are several different things to do:

Key Features to get you used to playing in the key

Make Music in which you can develop and explore musical ideas

Workouts to exercise your fingers and hands

Read and Play where there are a number of short pieces to play – read the title, work out the rhythm, find the notes and, when you're ready, play the piece right through without stopping!

Towards the end of the book you'll find **More Pieces to Play**, including some longer pieces, and duets and a trio to play with your friends.

Enjoy Joining the Dots!

Alan Bullard

Richard Wright

C major

Key Features

- Practise the first four bars in two ways, *tirando* and *apoyando*, always starting with the correct RH finger
- When you play these four bars *tirando*, rest the thumb on the D string

- For the first four bars, rest *m* and *a* on the G and B strings

Workouts

- Practise these workouts to warm up in the key of C major

- Look out for the different articulation in bars 1 and 3

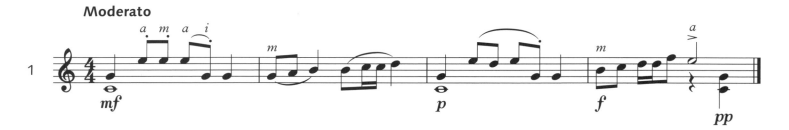

- Position the right hand carefully at the start of bars 1, 3 and 5

Make Music

Hop, Skip and Jump

- Make up a piece in the key of C major, starting as shown
- Aim for a length of eight bars

> - You could repeat the musical ideas at different pitches
> - Think about where the 'hop, skip and jump' might be in your piece
> - Consider contrasts in dynamics and articulation

Allegretto

mf

Summer Morning

- Tap this rhythm several times
- When you can do it, make the rhythm into a tune in the key of C major
- Start on any note of the scale and finish on the note C

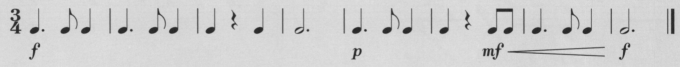

Allegro

f　　　　　　　*p*　　　*mf* ——— *f*

Read and Play

Poem

Andante cantabile

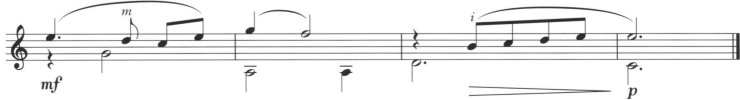

Black Beetle and Greenfly

Country Dance

Following the Footsteps

• Here's a piece to play with a friend
• The second player plays the same music, beginning when the first player reaches the asterisk sign (✳)

Key Features

- Practise the first four bars in two ways, *tirando* and *apoyando*, always starting with the correct RH finger
- When you play these four bars *tirando*, rest the thumb on the D string

- For the first four bars, rest *m* and *a* on the G and B strings

Workouts

- Practise these workouts to warm up in the key of A minor

- Look out for the different articulation in bars 1 and 3

- Make sure you move the LH thumb each time you change position

A minor

Make Music

Skating Slowly

- Make up a piece in the key of A minor, starting as shown
- Aim for a length of eight bars

- You could repeat the musical ideas at different pitches
- Try using the same patterns across different strings
- Consider contrasts in dynamics and articulation

Pacing Round and Round

- Make up a piece in the key of A minor by adding your own continuation of the melody
- Try out the thumb part on its own first
- You might like to imagine an animal pacing around a cage

Read and Play

A Minor Incident

8

Sarabande for J.S.B.

Andante

mp espress.

Two Mice

Daintily

Lively Conversation

- Here's a piece to play with a friend
- The second player plays the same music, beginning when the first player reaches the asterisk sign (✱)

Allegretto

G major

Key Features

- Practise the first four bars in two ways, *tirando* and *apoyando*, always starting with the correct RH finger
- When you play these four bars *tirando*, rest the thumb on the D string

- For the first four bars, rest *m* and *a* on the G and B strings

Workouts

- Practise these workouts to warm up in the key of G major

- Look out for the different articulation in bars 1 and 3

- Make sure the RH finger-pairings speak simultaneously
- Listen carefully to produce a balanced sound between them

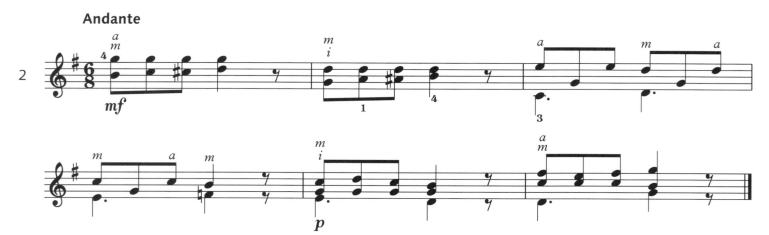

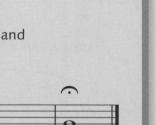

> • Imagine a lively conversation, in which there's so much to say that the sentences never get finished!
> • You could try turning bar 1 upside down or repeating the ideas at different pitches

Make Music

Phone a Friend!

- Make up a piece in the key of G major, starting as shown
- Aim for a length of eight bars

Enjoying the View

- Make up a piece in the key of G major by adding your own continuation of the melody
- Try out the thumb part on its own first
- You could imagine that you are at the top of a hill, looking over a vast expanse of land

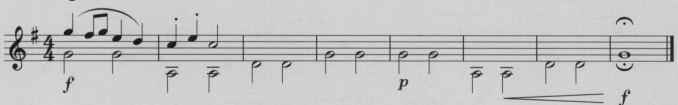

Read and Play

A Stately Occasion

G major

Chitter-Chatter

Allegretto leggiero

Interrupted Sleep

Andante

mp cantabile

Springtime

- Here's a piece to play with a friend
- The second player plays the same music, beginning when the first player reaches the asterisk sign (✱)

Allegretto lirico

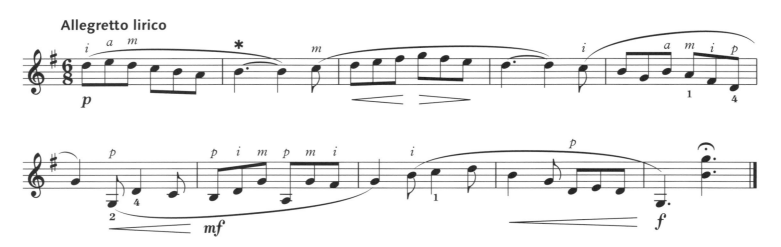

Key Features

- Practise the first four bars in two ways, *tirando* and *apoyando*, always starting with the correct RH finger
- When you play these four bars *tirando*, rest the thumb on the D string

- For the first four bars, rest the RH fingers on the D, G and B strings

Workouts

- Practise these workouts to warm up in the key of E minor

- Look out for the different articulation in bars 1 and 3

- Release the 4th finger as you reach for the C

E minor

Make Music

Gathering Clouds

- Make up a piece in the key of E minor, starting as shown
- Aim for a length of eight bars

> - Aim to communicate the feeling of a storm building up
> - You could imagine that the loud sections are rumbling thunder and the quiet notes are raindrops

Adagio

Melting Snow

- Make up a piece in the key of E minor by adding your own continuation of the melody
- Try out the thumb part on its own first

Andante espressivo

Read and Play

Sprint to the Finish

Fast and rhythmic

14

Call of the Homeland

Andante espressivo

Waking Up

Allegretto

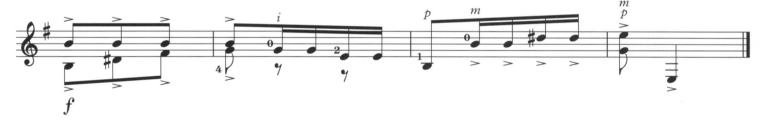

Interrupted Conversation

- Here's a piece to play with a friend
- The second player plays the same music, beginning when the first player reaches the asterisk sign (✱)

Lively

F major

Key Features

- Practise the first four bars in two ways, *tirando* and *apoyando*, always starting with the correct RH finger
- When you play these four bars *tirando*, rest the thumb on the A string
- The last two notes may be played with a half-barré, or by lifting the first finger from the C to the F

- For the first four bars, rest *a* on the G string

Workouts

- Practise these workouts to warm up in the key of F major

- Look out for the different articulation in bars 1 and 3

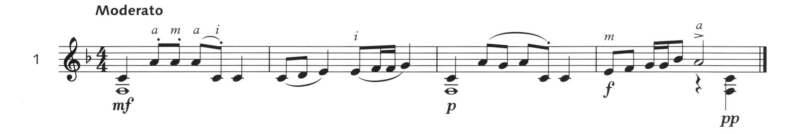

- The repeated semiquavers should be as accurate and even as possible!

> • Try repeating the rhythms at different pitches
> • Aim to keep the music moving steadily, and try to imagine the dancing

Make Music

Village Fair

• Make up a piece in the key of F major, starting as shown
• Aim for a length of eight bars

Dancing

Jumping in the Pool

• Tap this rhythm several times
• When you can do it, make the rhythm into a tune in the key of F major
• Start on any note of the scale and finish on the note F

Lively

Read and Play

Pausing for Thought

Scherzando

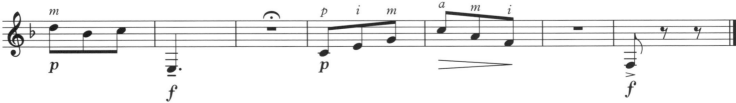

F major

Aria

Moderato cantabile

The Village Church

Andante

A Merry March

• Here's a piece to play with a friend
• The second player plays the same music, beginning when the first player reaches the asterisk sign (✱)

Allegro risoluto

18

Key Features

- Practise the first four bars in two ways, *tirando* and *apoyando*, always starting with the correct RH finger
- When you play these four bars *tirando*, rest the thumb on the A string

- For the first four bars, rest *m* and *a* on the G and B strings

Workouts

- Practise these workouts to warm up in the key of D minor

- Look out for the different articulation in bars 1 and 3

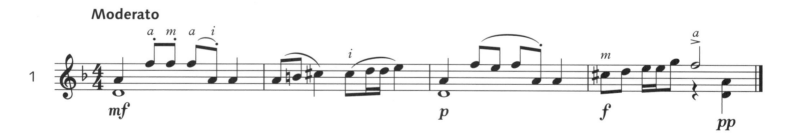

- Aim for even, legato articulation throughout this piece

D minor

Make Music

Here and There

- Make up a piece in the key of D minor, starting as shown
- Aim for a length of eight bars

> • Imagine two animals running about, chasing each other
> • You could suggest the mood by alternating fingers and thumb, as at the beginning
> • Remember to use dynamics to help with the musical character

Scurrying

Marching Boots

- Make up a piece in the key of D minor by adding your own continuation of the melody
- Try out the thumb part on its own first

Heavily

Read and Play

Open Spaces

Andante e legato

The Haunted Forest

On your Bike!

Slithery Snake

- Here's a piece to play with a friend
- The second player plays the same music, beginning when the first player reaches the asterisk sign (✱)

D major

Key Features

- Practise the first four bars in two ways, *tirando* and *apoyando*, always starting with the correct RH finger
- When you play these four bars *tirando*, rest the thumb on the A string

- For the first four bars, rest *m* and *a* on the G and B strings

Workouts

- Practise these workouts to warm up in the key of D major

- Look out for the different articulation in bars 1 and 3

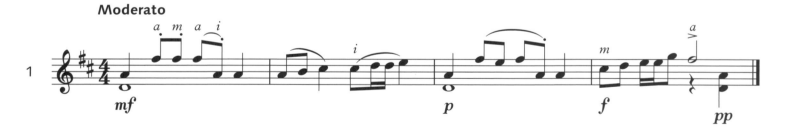

- Make sure all the LH fingertips approach the string from the same height

Make Music

Ducks on the Lake

- Make up a piece in the key of D major, starting as shown
- Aim for a length of eight bars

- Aim to create a picture of the bobbing and quacking ducks
- Think about how you could use contrasts in dynamics and articulation

At a moderate speed, with humour

Brass Band

- Make up a piece in the key of D major by adding your own continuation of the melody
- Try out the thumb part on its own first

Alla marcia

Read and Play

Reflections

Andante

Come Skate with Me

Bandstand

Minuet for Two

- Here's a piece to play with a friend
- The second player plays the same music, beginning when the first player reaches the asterisk sign (✱)

Key Features

- Practise the first four bars in two ways, *tirando* and *apoyando*, always starting with the correct RH finger
- When you play these four bars *tirando*, rest the thumb on the D string

- For the first four bars, rest *m* and *a* on the G and B strings

Workouts

- Practise these workouts to warm up in the key of A major

- Look out for the different articulation in bars 1 and 3

Moderato

- Make sure the staccato quavers are exactly the same length

Giocoso

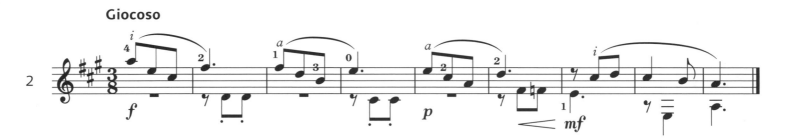

Make Music

Antique Dance

- Make up a piece in the key of A major, starting as shown
- Aim for a length of eight bars

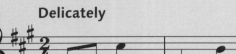

> • Imagine an old-time dance, gentle and graceful, with the dancers gliding past in their smart jackets and long dresses
> • Create a feeling of direction in the music, with crescendos and diminuendos

Irish Jig

- Tap this rhythm several times
- When you can do it, make the rhythm into a tune in the key of A major
- Start on any note of the scale and finish on the note A

Relaxing in the Sun

- Make up a piece in the key of A major by adding your own continuation of the melody
- Try out the thumb part on its own first
- Add your own expression marks
- Notice the pauses in the second line – take time to relax here!

Read and Play

Rambling Rupert

The Chimes Waltz

Out of my Way!

A major

Trumpets and Drums

Con brio

Wandering Free

Andante espressivo

Lullaby

- Here's a piece to play with a friend
- The second player plays the same music, beginning when the first player reaches the asterisk sign (✱)

Gently and calmly

- On the remaining pages you will find a variety of solo pieces of different lengths, and some duets and a trio to play with your friends
- You can use these for playing at sight, or as pieces to learn on your own or with your teacher
- Don't forget to check the key signature and time signature, and to get the fingers of both hands in place on the strings before you start

A Sad Memory

View from a Hill

More Pieces to Play

Restless Romance

Barn Dance

Forest Fanfares

Contentment

More Pieces to Play

Underground Train

With a steady rock beat

Smoothie

Gentle ragtime

Player 1

Player 2

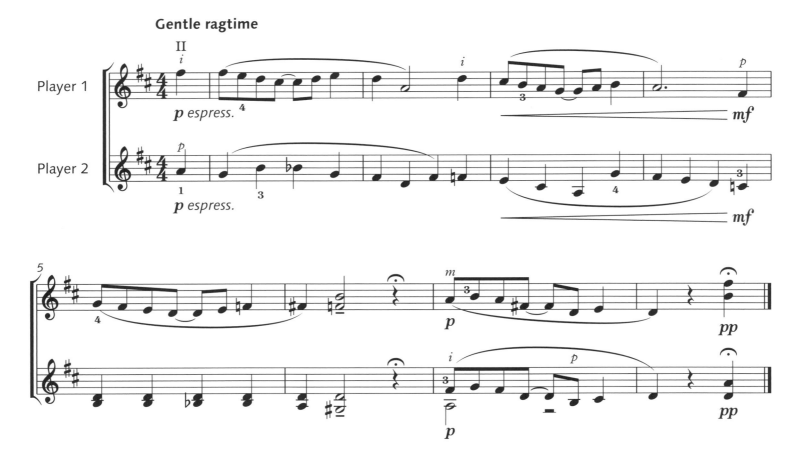

Clog Dance

At a moderate speed, but with energy

Lost in Thought...

More Pieces to Play

Tango for Three